A Gift For:

_____

From:

_____

Published by Hallmark Gift Books,
a division of Hallmark Cards, Inc.,
Kansas City, MO 64141
Visit us on the Web at www.Hallmark.com.

Editor: Emily Osborn
Art Director: Kevin Swanson
Designer: Brian Pilachowski
Production Artist: Dan Horton

ISBN: 978-1-59530-438-4
BOK4386

Printed and bound in China

FOR YOU, Mom, with LOVE

BY Melvina Young

GIFT BOOKS

You've gone from
tear wiper
and "boo-boo" kisser

to advice giver
and
best friend.

"You first," is what you said.

"Love you always," is what you meant.

You
always know what
I need

even before I do.

WHAT a
mother
says:

DON'T wipe that ON THERE!

DON'T stick that up YOUR NOSE!

TAKE that back outside!

WHAT a
MOTHER
means:

I'll love you, NO MATTER what.

"Look
at me,
mom!"

And you would, smiling
with pride and patience,
whether I was showing you something
for the first time
or for the thousandth.

You brushed love into my hair
with strong hands and gentle fingers
and told me I was beautiful.

You dried my tears
with tenderness and gentle words
of faithful love.

You helped me
find my own strength
and sent me off to find out
who I was.

I love you
for that.

"That's my child!"
you would say with pride.

It was times
like that when I felt proud
that you were mine, too.

I didn't always realize
that my shoes might be
a little NEWER than yours.
Or that my food was
a little WARMER.
Or my clothes were
a little more STYLISH.
Until later.

Thank you.

You built a beautiful house for us on
a strong foundation.

Where we lived,
there was warmth between the walls
and laughter under our roof.

Where we lived,
there was
l♥ve.

Roots, wings, hugs, smiles,
songs, stories, comfort, advice,
reassurance, love . . .

You gave
it all.

Just for the record—

store-bought
cookies
were fine.

The love was made from scratch.

You know that thing about my friends and "jumping off bridges"?

Thanks
for being
my
bungee
cord.

Even when I made it hard to love me . . .

you
did.

By being who you are,
you help me remember
who I am.

You not only made it okay to be me . . .

you made it
great
to be me.

That's meant everything.

How did you know

who I was

before I could figure out
who I was?

WWMD—
"What Would Mom Do?"

In one way or another, you are always my point of reference.

If it was important to

me . . .

you made it
important to
you.

For every "I told you so"
you could have said but didn't—

I l♥ve you.

Now I've told you so.

In all the world's uncertainty,

the certainty of

your l♥ve

has always anchored me.

You have
NERVES of
steel.

Otherwise,
I would have WORN
through them.

Sometimes your love
comes as patience,
and sometimes it
comes as pride.

Sometimes your love
comes as a smile,
and sometimes
it comes as tears.

Sometimes it comes
as acceptance—
or even disapproval.

But your love has always come
as an unbroken constant
in my life.

You've been an endless source of love.
Whether it was the soft love
of ENCOURAGEMENT
or the tougher love of CORRECTION,
the smooth love of PRAISE or
the rougher love of hard truth,

your love is an
endless
and
profound
love.

Sometimes when you like somebody,
you'll tell them what they
WANT TO HEAR.

It's when you love them
that you'll tell them what they
NEED TO HEAR.

Even when it's hard.

Thanks
for **loving me**
through
the hard stuff.

You mastered the art of multitasking—

working hard at work,
harder at home and,
hardest of all,
at loving me.

If it ever seemed
like I didn't appreciate you,
it's because you made
the "MOTHER" thing
look so easy.

I know that now.

You gave me more of

you

so that

I could be more

Me.

You opened doors
and windows
and said,

"The **world**
is yours."

When I was going through the "moody years,"
I must have really tested
YOUR PATIENCE.

Thanks
for sticking
by me.

Between all my mood swings and eye rolls,

where did you find space to fit all that

l♥ve?

All the things that make you a good MOM

make you a **fabulous** friend.

Mom-sized love . . .

built to last.

With the simple force of

your l♥ve,

you turned me into

a treasured human being,

OUR HOUSE
into a home,
and the world
INTO A SAFE PLACE.

You never doubted that my dreams
would one day become reality.

What I am,
you helped
me to be.

What I'll always REMEMBER are

your solid
support and
constant love.

You showed me
that STRENGTH and BRAVERY
are important things to have.

You taught me
that HARD WORK and INTEGRITY
build a person's character.

And you let me know
that **your love**
would
always be there.

You are
soft in heart,

tender in spirit,
and fierce
in faith.

As my mother, you showed me
the person I could be—

I was inspired by your
strength and wisdom.
I valued your

guidance.

As my friend, you understand
the person I am now—

I appreciate your
laughter and listening.
I value your
conversation and companionship.

Your love is as
powerful
as a hurricane
and as soothing
as a breeze.

MOM,
thanks for LOVING me
IN **so many**
good ways.

I'd like to think I inherited your best features.

You think
k*indness
and strength
are part of DNA?

Being a mother takes
an exceptional kind of love.

BUT THEN . . .
you're an
exceptional
kind of
woman.

You meet
the hard times
and the happy ones
with the same

love,
devotion,
and
determination.

Beautifully beautiful.

That's how you are.

That's how you taught me
to see the world.

There's a reason some people
think they can do anything . . .

they listened
to their
mothers.

I never had to look to
the horizon for a hero.

You've
always been
right here.

Everything good in me

started with your love.

You've worn a lot of caps as a mom . . .

They all say

"love"

on the front.

We don't always see
eye to eye . . .

we've found
heart to heart
is enough.

I walked my first steps
holding onto your fingertips
and danced my first steps
on the toes of your shoes.

Some of the most

important
steps in life

you helped me take.

By your **love,**

you inspire me to do loving things.

By your **patience,**

you move me to grow mine.

By your **wisdom**,

you encourage me to know more.

BY YOUR *friendship* . . .

I am blessed.

You think the 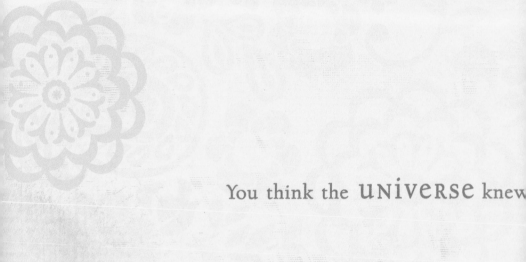 UNIVERSE knew

you were the
mother
I needed?

When I was little,
I thought you knew everything.
When I was a teenager,
I thought I knew everything.
Now that I'm an adult, I realize
there's a word for that
"everything" you knew:

It's called
wisdom.

If I held
an audition for
"My Dream
Mom,"

you'd take center stage
and own it.

You never tried to be my peer—

NO POSING,
no "hip" talk,
NO WEIRDNESS—

but you were always my friend.

As I've gotten older,
I've come to realize
something that astounds me—

Not everybody has
the kind of MOTHER I do.

Not everybody has
the kind of love I have known.

I feel privileged
to have *you*
in my life.

BY EXAMPLE, YOU TAUGHT ME
TO WORK HARD,
TREAT PEOPLE RIGHT,
FIND LOVE,

KNOW joy,
keep my head up,
and keep my eyes on the prize.

A mom
who'd do anything
for her children—

that's the kind of mother
you've always been.

Even though you don't play favorites . . .

thanks

FOR MAKING ME feel

like yours.

You know all those times
 you made me feel like a good and
well-loved person?

Your turn.

Only a mom would let you pay her back
for her hard work and sacrifice

with a
hug.

Remember when everything you did EMBARRASSED me?

I'm really
embarrassed
about that
now.

There is no one special day
when I'm thankful for you
or wish I could give you something special
to show my love.

Unless every day
is special.

The only thing better than getting you as a MOM

is getting to know you as the

cool woman
you are.

You've got words

that feel like

hugs

and
hugs
that feel like
home.

I know you'd stand with me
through hell, high water, the creek rising,
no paddle, rough seas, the tide turning,
or any other hard time.

I know . . .
because *you*
always have.

If you have enjoyed this book
or it has touched your life in some way,
we would love to hear from you.

Please send your comments to:
Hallmark Book Feedback
P.O. Box 419034
Mail Drop 215
Kansas City, MO 64141
Or e-mail us at:
booknotes@hallmark.com